We know that you're a friend so true,
We're looking forward to playing with you!
Come a little closer and take a look,
Open the pages of this fun-filled book.

Games and activities you will find,
So many things to pass the time.
So let the fairy fun begin,
Unfurl your wings and flutter in!

Please keep this book safe from pesky goblins!

This
Rainbow Magic
Annual belongs to

....

....

ORCHARD BOOKS
338 Euston Road, London NW1 3BH
Orchard Books Australia
Level 17/207 Kent Street, Sydney, NSW 2000

First published in 2013 by Orchard Books.

A CIP catalogue record for this book is available
from the British Library.

ISBN 978 1 408 32817 0

3 5 7 9 10 8 6 4 2

Printed in China
Orchard Books is a division of Hachette Children's Books,
an Hachette UK company

www.hachette.co.uk

Adult supervision is recommended when glue, paint, scissors and
other sharp points are in use.

Fairy
Annual
2014

*Fabulous fairies are waiting
for you inside!*

Contents

Hello, Fairy Friend!

We're so looking forward to having lots of magical fun and games with you!

Inside this book are all of your favourite Rainbow Magic fairies, ready to share activities, games, top tips and sweet secrets with you.

The only problem is that mean Jack Frost has been up to his old tricks again. When we wouldn't let him and his goblins have any more of our delicious sweet treats, the greedy things stole our special charms! Can you help us to find them? The goblins dropped them into the pages of the book as they ran away.

We know you'll love reading the annual, and good luck finding our sweets!

Lots of love and tickly fairy kisses,

Esme
x

Clara
x

Lottie
x

Coco
x

Nina
x

Layla
x

Madeleine
x

A Sprinkling of Rainbow Magic

The seven Rainbow Fairies have each cast a special friendship spell for you. Try reading them out to your best friend!

Write down some of the nicest things your best friend has ever done for you and the things you like most about them.

Ruby the Red Fairy

My spell is for smiles
and a thousand kinds of
Making a friend
is a wonderful pact!

Amber the Orange Fairy

My spell is for fun
and meeting to play.
Chatting with friends
will brighten your day!

Saffron the Yellow Fairy

My spell is for being
there no matter what.
A friend you can count on
is worth such a lot!

Good times and bad...

When Jack Frost didn't get invited to the Midsummer Ball, he caused so much trouble! The Ice Lord took the colours away from Fairyland by banishing the Rainbow Fairies to the human world. Thank goodness Kirsty and Rachel were there to help them – true friends in times of need!

Heather the Violet Fairy

My spell is for help, splitting problems in two. You never know when your friend may need you.

Izzy the Indigo Fairy

My spell is for giggles, for laughs in the sun. Friendship is priceless, but most of all fun!

Sky the Blue Fairy

My spell is for whispers and secrets to share. Open your heart to someone who'll care.

Fern the Green Fairy

My spell is for trying out daring new things. Do them together – you'll be lifted on wings!

Right Royal Words

Can you help Elizabeth the Jubilee Fairy find ten royal words in the grid below? The words you are searching for are listed at the bottom of the page. They could be upside down or backwards, so look carefully!

```
A D S P T N X Q U L P
C L L P N Z Q L U P A
Y E M A I R S L L T L
Z Z L G Y N Y A S H A
V N R E G W I B L R C
O I P A B O S T Y O E
W N C N W R O N F N T
R D S T Z C A S P E J
O V D S W E X T H M X
Y B A B H J N G I E R
A S F E Q Y T R C O B
L J F P A R T Y Z P L N
P E Q D W Z C N K M F
K P Z O G W L F G L Y
B A N Q U E T Z I X S
```

WORDS TO SPOT:

banquet, celebration, royal, party, crown, palace, ball, throne, reign, pageant.

Florence's BFF!

All of the Rainbow Magic fairies are super friendly, but who would be your best fairy friend (BFF) in the Rainbow Magic world? Take the quiz below to find out.

How would you describe your personality?

A. Confident
B. Friendly but shy
C. Funny. You love to make people laugh!
D. Relaxed and easy-going

What do you like to do the most on a Saturday night?

A. Make up dance routines and listen to music
B. Chill out with your friends in your bedroom
C. Write jokes and stories
D. Read your favourite fairy book

Which of these flowers do you like the best?

A. Poppy
B. Rose
C. Iris
D. Sunflower

What is your favourite colour?

A. Red
B. Pink
C. Purple
D. Yellow

What is your favourite animal?

A. Dog
B. Cat
C. Pony
D. Rabbit

Mostly A's – Your BFF is Una the Concert Fairy
You're happy and have lots of energy, just like Una! You're also very loyal and always stand by your friends.

Mostly B's – Your BFF is Mia the Bridesmaid Fairy
You're very friendly with a gorgeous smile, just like Mia! You look after your friends and would never give away a secret.

Mostly C's – Your BFF is Leah the Theatre Fairy
You and Leah both have a brilliant sense of humour. You're confident but also like time to chill out on your own.

Mostly D's – Your BFF is Hannah the Happy Ever After Fairy
You have a wonderful imagination. You and Hannah would make great writing partners! Your pals always love to spend time with you.

11

An Enchanted Animal Adventure

Part 1

"Please can you pass me the green felt-tip pen?" asked Kirsty Tate, smiling at her best friend Rachel Walker. The girls were in Kirsty's bedroom drawing a picture of their pets: Buttons, Rachel's dog and Pearl, Kirsty's cat. Rachel and Buttons were staying with Kirsty for a week over the summer holidays. As Rachel gave Kirsty the pen, she noticed a flurry of sparkles around it.

"It looks like fairy magic!" whispered Rachel. The two friends were lucky enough to have had lots of amazing adventures with the Rainbow Magic fairies. Could this be the start of another one…?

The sparkles surrounded the two girls and suddenly two little fairies appeared in front of them. It was their old friends Katie the Kitten Fairy and Bella the Bunny Fairy!

"We're so pleased to see you!" cried Bella, doing a tiny somersault in the air as her bunny, Misty, turned all the colours of the rainbow.

Katie told the girls that it was almost time for the annual Rainbow Magic Animal Show to begin in the grounds of the Fairyland Palace.

"This year we'd like you to be honorary judges!" Katie smiled. "And King Oberon and Queen Titania have said that we can use our special Pet Keeper magic so Buttons and Pearl can come along too!"

Rachel and Kirsty exchanged delighted glances. They loved visiting Fairyland and now their best animal friends could visit as well.

The girls cuddled their pets as Bella and Katie joined their wands together.

"On this special, magical day,
Pets come to Fairyland for fun and play!"

A whirlwind surrounded them all. The girls felt themselves shrinking as tiny wings appeared on their backs. Soon they were flying through the skies of Fairyland.

"Oh, I just love being a fairy!" cried Rachel, flying a loop-the-loop.

"And just look at Buttons and Pearl!" Kirsty laughed. The girls' pets had tiny wings too and were chasing each other round and round in the air!

As the girls flew closer to the turrets of the Fairyland Palace, they spotted lots of their Rainbow Magic friends getting ready for the show. Pearl the Cloud Fairy was making fluffy white clouds look like different animals, and Mara the Meerkat Fairy's meerkat friend was practising a complicated dance routine with the rest of his family.

Bella and Katie led the girls to their seats next to the king and queen's thrones in the palace courtyard. The fairies explained that the show had two different classes. The first was a Skills Class where each animal showed off their special ability. The second was a Best of Friends Class, where the fairies and animals worked together to produce a spectacular performance.

Just then, a loud cackle filled the air and a huge snowball flew past, narrowly missing King Oberon. Rachel and Kirsty exchanged an alarmed glance. What on earth was happening?

Turn to page 32 to see what happens next!

Meet Lottie the Lollipop Fairy

My lollies taste lovely! Apart from when mean Jack Frost and his goblins are around...

Personality
Smiley and full of giggles.

Favourite place in Fairyland
The Fairyland Sweet Factory.

Favourite colour
All the colours of the rainbow.

Yummiest food
Exotic fruit salad, lemon drizzle cake and ice lollies.

Favourite fairy friend
Lizzie the Sweet Treats Fairy.

Most trusted magic
With a wave of her wand, Lottie's lollipops can taste of any flavour!

Fairy Outfit
Lottie's dress shows off some of her favourite colours. She teams it with a pair of pink wedges. Matilda the Hair Stylist Fairy sometimes helps Lottie try out different styles with her wavy blonde hair.

Lottie and the Sweet Fairies work with Honey the Sweet Fairy. They make sure that all sweet treats in Fairyland and the human world taste delicious.

14

Petal Personality!

The Petal Fairies are always busy keeping their blooms beautiful! Answer the questions in this flowchart to find out which flowery fairy you're most like.

Are you a do-er or a dreamer?

Do-er — *Dreamer*

Are you happiest alone or in a crowd?

Do you prefer fun fashion or old favourites?

Alone — *Crowd* — *Fashion* — *Faves*

Do you prefer to be a trendsetter or everyone's friend?

Are you happiest centre-stage or behind the scenes?

Is your style classic or funky?

Do you like garden games or country walks?

Trendsetter — *Friend* — *Stage* — *Behind* — *Classic* — *Funky* — *Games* — *Walks*

| Hot-house flower | Big-hearted bloom | Rare beauty | Queen of the garden | Ray of sunshine | Super in scarlet | Flowery friend | Blushing bud |

Olivia the Orchid Fairy
An eye-catching beauty who always attracts a crowd!

Ella the Rose Fairy
Sometimes shy, but blessed with natural grace and a sweet manner.

Danielle the Daisy Fairy
The good-hearted girl-next-door whom everybody loves to love!

Sparkly Snowflake Cards

These wonderful wintry cards will make your friends feel super-special! Each one has a unique snowflake design, plus a gorgeous bow. As a finishing touch, I always use a matching glitter pen to write a message inside.

Gabriella the Snow Kingdom Fairy
xxx

STAY SAFE!
Always ask a grown-up to help you cut the paper, card and ribbon.

You will need:

2 sheets of white paper

Scissors

Coloured card (28cm x 14cm)

Coloured ribbon

PVA glue

Glitter

Plates or tins to help draw perfect circles (optional)

Newspaper

Step 1
Fold the card in half to make a square. Draw a circle on one half of the card and cut it out. Set it aside to use in the next step. Smear some glue on the front of the card (the side with the hole) and sprinkle on some glitter. Allow to dry.

Step 2

Draw a smaller circle on the circle of card and cut out. Then use this smaller circle as a template to cut out a circle of white paper.

Step 3

Fold the circle of white paper in half and then in half again two or three more times. Cut out shapes, then unfold to reveal your snowflake.

Step 4

Use some glue to stick the snowflake onto the small circle of card. Allow to dry.

Step 5

Lay the card face down on newspaper. Centre the snowflake face down in the hole. Glue the ribbon to the back of the snowflake and to the card above and below. Trim the extra ribbon off.

Step 6

Glue a 14 cm square piece of white paper inside the card behind the snowflake. Use another ribbon to tie a pretty bow and glue it to the front of the card. Allow to dry, then write a message to your friend inside.

True or False?

Have a good look at this happy fairy scene and decide whether the statements below are true or false.

 1 Ruby the Red Fairy and Olivia the Orchid Fairy are having tea inside the old black pot.

 2 Izzy the Indigo Fairy is sitting inside the log.

3 There are fourteen fairies in this scene.

4 The bees are playing with Danielle the Daisy Fairy.

5 The ladybird has a pink tummy.

6 Jack Frost is spying on the fairies from the pond.

Meet Jack Frost and the Goblins

Jack Frost has an army of naughty goblins to help him create chaos. Whenever there's a chill in the air, the fairies must be on their guard...

Name
Jack Frost.

Favourite colour
Ice-white.

Personality
Cold-hearted, jealous and mean.

Home
The frozen Ice Castle.

Frosty friends
His band of grumpy goblin servants.

Most trusted magic
His powerful banishment spell.

Frosty features
A chill breeze always swirls around Jack's bony figure. His ice-blue robes are trimmed with sharp icicles and frost glints in his white hair and beard. His pointy elf boots leave icy footprints behind him.

Horrible hobby
Jack thinks he's a magnificent artist. He's always etching frozen designs on window panes, but the fact that no one ever notices them never fails to put him in a frosty mood!

Name
The Goblins.

Personality
Selfish and sneaky but very dim.

Home
The goblin town at the foot of Jack Frost's Ice Castle.

Favourite food
Goblins are so greedy they'll eat anything, even dog food!

Horrible hobby
Stealing fairy possessions and trampling on flowers.

Frosty friends
None. They even fight amongst themselves.

Worst time of year
Winter! Jack Frost gives them lots of jobs to do and goblins hate having cold feet!

Frosty features
The tallest goblins come up to Kirsty and Rachel's shoulders. But Jack Frost can use his powers to make the goblins taller or smaller! All goblins are ugly green creatures with big feet and pointy ears and noses.

* We're always ready to cause mischief!

Meet Esme
the Ice Cream Fairy

My ice cream is so delicious it can be eaten at any time of the year!

Personality
Fun-loving and loyal.

Favourite place in Fairyland
The shady palace gardens, where ice cream stays nice and cool.

Favourite colour
Yellow, just like the creamiest vanilla ice cream.

Yummiest food
Pepperoni pizza and ice cream sundaes.

Most trusted magic
Esme's magic means you can eat as much ice cream as you like without ever getting full. Hurray!

Favourite fairy friend
Kate the Royal Wedding Fairy.

Fairy Outfit
Esme's bright jeans and candy-striped top complement her olive skin. Her high-top sneakers are super-comfortable and she likes to magically change their colour with a wave of her wand!

Every year in Fairyland on Treat Day, Esme and the other sweet Fairies work very hard to make a basket of delicious treats for each and every fairy.

Dress-up Time!

Using your pencils and felt-tip pens, dress Kate the Royal Wedding Fairy in a fabulous outfit.

Christmas Tree Decorations

Every year my friend Stella the Star Fairy flutters over to help me make these tree decorations. The shimmery shapes always get us in a Christmassy mood! Why not make the shapes gold, silver or even rainbow-coloured?

Holly the Christmas Fairy
xx

STAY SAFE!
Always ask a grown-up to help you. Never use scissors on your own.

You will need:
Coloured or patterned paper

Scissors

PVA glue

Ribbon

Selection of glitter glue, glitter, beads and sequins
(optional decorations)

Step 1
Fold a piece of paper and draw one half of a star or heart. Cut it out and open up the shape. This is the template for your decoration.

Step 2
Use the template to draw and cut out three more identical shapes. Fold each one exactly in half.

Step 3
Put all the shapes together and cut a small hole near the top.

Step 4
Glue the back of one half of a shape to the back of another half, matching it as closely as possible.

Step 5
Then glue the back of the other half of the shape and do the same again. Keep doing this until all the shapes are glued together and you have a complete star. Leave to dry.

Step 6
Decorate your shapes and thread ribbon through the hole at the top. Hang on your tree using the ribbon loop.

Meet Coco
the Cupcake Fairy

I was so upset when the goblins stole my magic charm and made my cupcakes taste yucky!

Personality
Sweet and kind.

Yummiest Food
Cheese twists and vanilla milkshakes.

Favourite colour
Pastel colours, just like her favourite cupcake toppings.

Most trusted magic
With a wave of her wand, Coco's magic makes all cakes extra-tasty!

Favourite place in Fairyland
The kitchens of the Fairyland Palace.

Favourite fairy friend
Cherry the Cake Fairy.

When Kirsty and Rachel tried to make cupcakes for Kirsty's birthday it was a disaster. So the girls went to a shop called Cupcake Corner instead, but the chef there was suspiciously green and mean!

Fairy Outfit
Coco's mini-skirt and motif top are fairy fabulous! Her long auburn hair gets in the way when she's baking cupcakes. So she piles it up, and with a whisper of magic words, adds a few sparkly hair jewels!

Spells for smiling

Whenever the fairies want to make someone smile, they create a happiness spell. Copy this one onto a piece of paper and pass it to a friend who needs cheering up!

To my friend so dear and true,
A Rainbow Magic wish for you.
Happy times, joy and care,
Shall follow you everywhere.

Fairy giggles, fun and laughter,
And a happy ever after.
May your days be filled with glee,
For you have given these to me!

Can you write a happiness
spell of your own?

madison

....
....
....
....
....
....
....

Fairy Fact File

My fairy name would be:

.... the ....Fairy.

The Rainbow Magic fairy
I love the best is:

....

....

The fairy that looks
most like me is:

....

....

The most exciting thing about
being a fairy would be:

....

....

....

....

My secret wish is:

Fluttery Frame

How would you look if you were a fairy?
Draw a picture of your fairy self in this frame, taking care to add wings
and a magic wand!

Meet Clara the Chocolate Fairy

My delicious chocolate cake is a favourite with all my fairy friends!

Yummiest food
Strawberries dipped in chocolate and chilli con carne with a little chocolate sprinkled into

Favourite place in Fairyland
The toadstool houses of fairy friends.

Personality
Funny and feisty.

Most trusted magic
Clara's fairy magic makes sure there's plenty of sweet treats for everyone.

Favourite colour
Anything gorgeous and glittery!

Favourite fairy friend
Honey the Sweet Fairy

It was such a disaster when chocolate everywhere started to taste horrible! Kirsty and Rachel helped Clara to get her magical cocoa bean charm back from Jack Frost.

Fairy Outfit
Clara looks ready to party in her sparkly outfit! Her purple tunic and short silver leggings make her blue eyes sparkle. Tyra the Dress Designer Fairy helped Clara to put her outfit together.

Green Means Go!

The Green Fairies are always on the move, making sure that fairies and humans look after their lands. Learn more about these special fairies and the world by solving the clues below.

Across

2 This is all around us. We breathe it in!

5 Edie loves to spend time in this special place.

6 Coral looks after this underwater place.

7 This sandy area is the perfect place to spend a sunny day.

Down

1 Many thousands of creatures live in this wet and tropical environment.

3 The planet where humans live.

4 A stream of water looked after by Milly.

31

Part 2

"You dratted fairies," cried a familiar, icy voice. It was Jack Frost, riding on an icebolt with two goblins by his side! "How dare you not invite me to your animal show? I'm going to teach you a lesson. My special animals will be the stars of the show!"

"What is Jack Frost up to now?" Kirsty whispered to Rachel. The naughty Ice Lord was always causing trouble!

Jack Frost pushed forward his two goblin servants, who were sniggering in a very suspicious manner. The smallest goblin was holding a huge fat slug that was snoring loudly!

"This is Sid," announced the small green creature, as he tickled the slug's tummy.

The other goblin, who had a large wart on his nose, held out a slimy toad. "This is Tony." He smirked. "And he's much cleverer than any of your silly fairy animals!"

The king and queen looked very surprised but declared the show open.

"All animals are welcome here," said King Oberon. "Let the fun begin!"

The audience clapped as the Skills Class began. And what a show it was!

Lily the Rainforest Fairy used her magic to call upon a host of her rainforest friends, including monkeys and parrots. They performed a stunning aerial display! Next, the Music Fairies and Anya the Cuddly Creatures Fairy sang a beautiful song, joined by a chorus of mews and woofs from the Pet Keeper pets.

"How do we choose a winner, Rachel?" asked Kirsty with a frown on her face. "All of the contestants are amazing."

But then, Tony the Toad waddled out with his goblin owner, and began to sing. The girls could hardly believe what they were hearing. It was so loud and out of tune that the girls and fairies had to cover their ears.

"RIIIBBBBETTTTT, CROOOOAKKKKK, HURROOOWWWWWW, BURRRRRRRRRRPPP!"

The only creatures enjoying the noise were the goblins and Jack Frost. All of the other animals fled, trying to escape from the terrible racket.

As the girls were wondering how they could stop the noise, clever Buttons bounded down to the performance area. He guided Tony and his goblin chum away from the palace and towards the Fairyland Forest. Phew! But there was still the Best of Friends Class to go. What other chaos would Jack Frost's horrible creatures cause?

Turn to page 54 to see how the story ends!

Stars in Your Eyes!

Destiny the Pop star Fairy just loves to read her fairy star sign. What does your star sign say about you?

AQUARIUS
(20th Jan – 18th Feb)
You are a very honest and loyal friend with an inventive streak. You often have lots of good ideas.

PISCES
(19th Feb – 20th March)
You have lots of creativity and imagination, though you can also be a bit of a dreamer.

VIRGO
(23rd Aug – 22nd Sept)
You are very clever and love to have chats and discussions about all kinds of subjects.

LIBRA
(23rd Sept – 22nd Oct)
You're so generous and kind, everyone wants to be your friend! You like to have plenty of time to think things through.

SCORPIO
(23rd Oct – 21st Nov)
You're very determined and if you want something, you work hard to get it! You are very passionate about the things you believe in.

TAURUS
(20th April – 20th May)
You're a great friend and give very good advice! You work hard, are extremely loyal and can be a bit stubborn!

ARIES
(21st March – 19th April)
You have lots of energy and like a new challenge. You perform really well in team sports.

GEMINI
(21st May – 20th June)
You're a chatterbox! You often change your mind at the last minute as you find it hard to make a decision.

CANCER
(21st June – 22nd July)
You can be quite shy but you are very loving and caring. You have a wonderful imagination and may like to paint.

LEO
(23rd July – 22nd Aug)
You are very organised and like to be in control. You make a brilliant leader and best friend.

CAPRICORN
(22nd Dec – 19th Jan)
You can be competitive and are often good at sports. You have a brilliant sense of humour and tell very funny jokes.

SAGITTARIUS
(22nd Nov – 21st Dec)
You like being surrounded by lovely things, and have many friends. You are creative and lots of fun to be around.

Meet Madeleine the Cookie Fairy

In my story, a goblin dinner lady was causing all sorts of trouble at Candy Land!

Personality
Confident and adventurous.

Favourite place in Fairyland
Playing with the animals in the Fairyland Forest.

Favourite colour
All bright and colourful patterns.

Most trusted magic
Madeleine's spell makes everyone feel warm and special after eating one of her delicious cookies.

Yummiest food
Spaghetti Bolognese, cookie-dough ice cream.

Favourite fairy friend
Leona the Unicorn Fairy.

Kirsty and Rachel tried to ice a special cookie in Madeleine's story, but it all went horribly wrong due to Jack Frost's meanness!

Fairy Outfit
Madeleine is a very adventurous dresser. Her colourful harem pants and comfy trainers show that she is always ready for action!

Goblin Joke File

Goblins are very naughty and they love to tell jokes and riddles! Here are some of their favourites.

How do you make milk shake?

Give it a good scare.

What steps would you take if Jack Frost was chasing you?

Great big ones.

Where does Bertram go to wash his hands?

The croakroom.

What kind of hair does Shannon the Ocean Fairy have?

Wavy.

What is a volcano?

A mountain with hiccups.

What followed Lauren the Puppy Fairy's pet?

His tail.

What is an insect's favourite sport?

Cricket.

Spot the Difference

Oh no! The naughty goblins have sneaked over from their jokes page and have sabotaged this picture of Natalie the Christmas Stocking Fairy. Can you spot the six differences in Picture 2?

38

Keep Fairy Fit!

Olympia the Games Fairy and the seven Sporty Fairies really enjoy keeping fit. Read their top tips and get fit the fun fairy way!

Get out and about!

There's nothing like being outside in the garden or park. Francesca the Football Fairy takes her ball with her everywhere. She works on her keepy-uppies or practises passes if she bumps into friends.

Tag team!

When she's not riding her pony, Helena the Horseriding Fairy likes to play a game of tag. She starts off by being It, and chases her friends until one is caught. Then they become It!

Time for tennis

Alice the Tennis Fairy loves to play tennis. Even when there's nobody to play with, she likes to practise. All she needs is a racquet, a ball and a wall. And she makes sure she isn't close to any windows!

Tough triathlon

In Olympia the Games Fairy's story, a triathlon took place in the human world. A triathlon is a very tough competition where competitors have to swim, ride a bike *and* run around a course. But you don't have to do all three activities together to keep fit: doing just one is also great exercise!

Super skates

Getting your skates on is a brilliant way to get around. Zoe the Skating Fairy is an expert. You'll need some-one to give you a hand at first.

Stay safe!

Always ask an adult before trying a new sport and before you leave the house or garden.

39

Meet Layla the Candyfloss Fairy

Favourite place in Fairyland
The Fairyland Palace.

Personality
Sweet and cheeky.

My sweet treat is a favourite at carnivals and fairs!

Yummiest food
Frothy hot chocolate with lots of pink marshmallows.

Most trusted magic
Making everyone smile after they enjoy a serving of tasty candyfloss.

Favourite fairy friend
Kylie the Carnival Fairy.

Favourite colour
Pink!

Candyfloss is usually pink, but in Layla's story the goblins are eating multi-coloured candyfloss! The girls and Layla had to stage a dramatic rescue to retrieve Layla's magic charm.

Fairy Outfit
Each time Layla flutters by in her hot pink dress, the delicious smell of candyfloss fills the air! Her pink-dipped hair is very fashionable. She likes to change the colour of her petticoats with a wave of her wand.

Clara's Sleepytime Chocolate

Here is Clara the Chocolate Fairy's recipe for a truly delicious hot, chocolaty drink. Yum! Just make sure you keep it out of the way of greedy goblins...

STAY SAFE!
Always ask a grown-up to help you when you're cooking.

For each guest you will need:

1 mug of milk

40 grams good-quality dark chocolate, broken into small pieces

What to do:

1 Pour the milk into a pan and ask an adult to help you heat it until it's almost bubbling.

2 Now remove your pan from the heat and tip in the chocolate. Stir gently until it all melts.

3 Carefully pour the hot chocolate into the mugs.

It might take a few minutes for your hot chocolate to be cool enough to drink. Lucky Abigail the Breeze Fairy can cool hers down in a second!

Animal Magic

Do you love animals, just like the Pet Keeper Fairies? Write here about your own pet, or the one you wish you had!

My pet's name:

Type of animal:

Colour:

Birthday:

Age:

Favourite toy:

Favourite food:

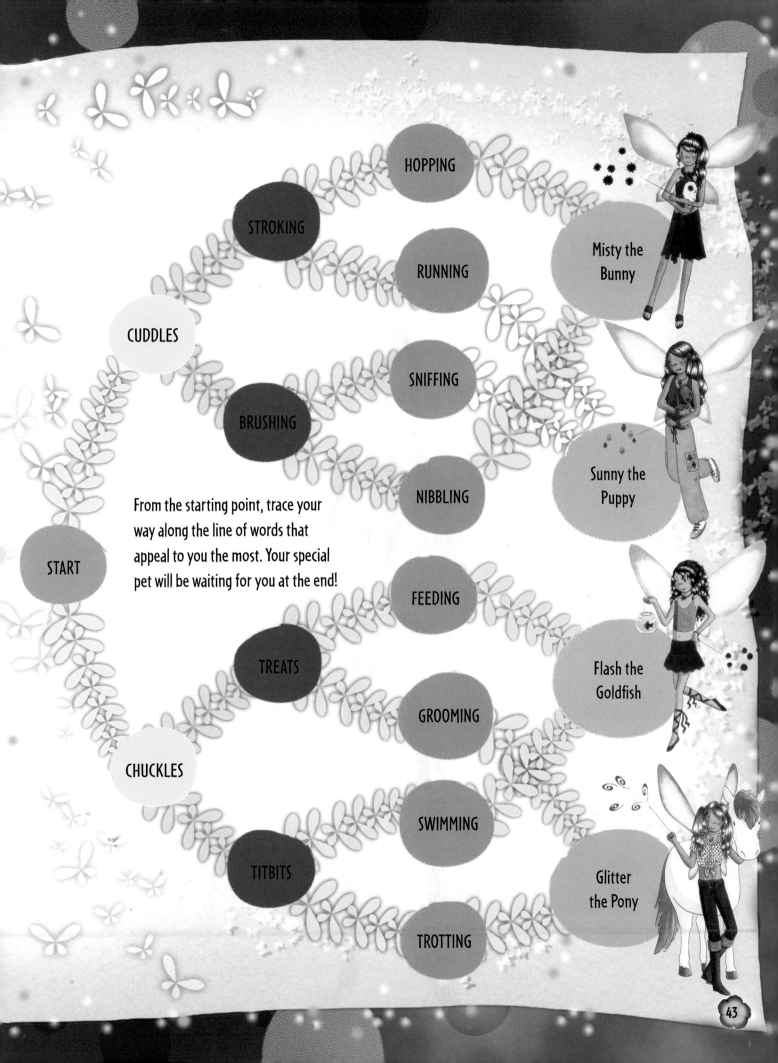

HOPPING

STROKING

RUNNING

CUDDLES

Misty the
Bunny

SNIFFING

BRUSHING

From the starting point, trace your
way along the line of words that
appeal to you the most. Your special
pet will be waiting for you at the end!

NIBBLING

Sunny the
Puppy

START

FEEDING

TREATS

Flash the
Goldfish

GROOMING

CHUCKLES

SWIMMING

TITBITS

Glitter
the Pony

TROTTING

43

Get Ruby Ready!

Ruby is going to a Midsummer Ball! Can you design her a new outfit to wear? Don't forget the all-important finishing touches such as shoes, jewellery and a bag.

44

Meet Jennifer the Babysitter Fairy

I had a really special adventure with Rachel and Kirsty at a brilliant place called EcoWorld!

Personality
Kind, caring and full of fun.

Favourite place in Fairyland
The Fairyland Nursery.

Yummiest food
Jacket potatoes piled with cheese, caramel popcorn and raspberry ripple ice cream.

Favourite colour
All the primary colours – especially red and blue!

Favourite fairy friend
Sabrina the Sweet Dreams Fairy.

Most trusted magic
Jennifer's magic makes sure that all children have lots of fun.

Fairy Outfit
Jennifer's outfit is bright and funky, but also very practical. Her denim shorts and leggings are super-comfy and her stripy tank top keeps her warm.

All of the Rainbow Magic fairies help Jennifer to look after the babies in the Fairyland Nursery. The Sporty Fairies teach them different sports and the Twilight Fairies help out at nap-time.

45

Kirsty's Meaning of Dreams

Everyone knows that dreams can come true!
Here Kirsty tells you what some dreams mean...

Fairies

If you dream about fairies, it means you are feeling relaxed and happy and will have lots of fun and giggles the next day.

Faces

Dreaming of happy smiling faces means you will have lots of luck.

Travelling by plane

Dreaming of flying in a plane could mean you'd like to travel lots when you're older.

Ants and bugs

If you dream about ants and bugs, it means that you work well in a team.

Apples

When your dream includes apples, it means that your friends will always be close to you.

Babies

If you have a dream about a baby, it could mean you are about to make a great new friend!

Birds

Dreaming of birds means that good things are going to happen! The brighter the feathers, the better the luck.

Butterflies

When you dream about a butterfly, it means you have made a good impression on a new person.

Ice

If you have a dream about ice, it means that you are feeling unsure about something.

Goblins

Dreaming about goblins means that someone is soon going to play a trick on you!

Friends

If you dream about a friend, it means you are going to have exciting adventures with them very soon.

Spiders

Believe it or not, spiders bring very good luck, so be happy if you dream about them!

Favourite fairy friend

Belle the Birthday Fairy.

Jack Frost almost ruined Kirsty's birthday in my special story!

Favourite colour

Red and yellow.

Most trusted magic

Nina's magic helps everyone enjoy their birthday party.

Favourite place in Fairyland

Anywhere where there's a party going on!

Yummiest food

Paella, mango slices.

Personality

Kind, warm and bubbly.

Fairy Outfit

Nina's bright outfit reflects her bubbly personality. She loves baking birthday cakes for her friends and covering them in magical birthday candles that change colour as they are blown out!

In Nina's story, she and the girls had to be very brave and face Jack Frost. Without Nina's magical charms, all birthday parties and cakes were a disaster!

Sunset Spell

Naughty Jack Frost has cast an icy spell on Ava the Sunset Fairy, causing her to fade away! Can you break his spell by completing this picture? Then colour in Ava using your brightest colours!

29
28 • • 30
27 • • 31
• 32
26 • • 33
25 • • 36 • 34
24 • • 9 • 35
23 • • 20 10
22 • 21 • 12 • 11
19 • 18 • 8 • 38 • 37
• 39
13 • 7
17 •
6 •
5
16 • •
14 • 1
• 2
15 • • 4
3 •

49

Ice Castle Snowglobe

This glittery globe reminds me of the ones the Rainbow Fairies gave to Kirsty and Rachel when the girls rescued them. The pesky pair! The icy dome will sparkle like snow every time you give it a shake. I hope you hate it!

From, Evil Jack Frost

Tip

Keep the snowglobe on a saucer in case any oil escapes!

You will need:

A small glass jar with lid
Plasticine or modelling clay
Permanent marker pen
Card
PVA glue
Baby oil
Glitter

STAY SAFE!

Always ask a grown-up to help you .

Step 1

Draw a picture of the Ice Castle onto card with permanent marker pen. Cut out the picture. The finished shape must fit inside your jar.

PVA GLUE

Step 2

Paint the front, back and edges of the card with three or four layers of PVA glue. Leave to dry between coats.

Step 3
Press modelling clay into the lid of the jar. Leave enough space around the edge so the lid still fits on the jar.

Step 4
Press your picture firmly into the clay. Fill the jar to the top with baby oil and add a big pinch of glitter.

Step 5
Screw the lid tightly back onto the jar. Wipe any oil off the outside of the jar. Use a strip of modelling clay to seal the join between the jar and the lid.

Step 6
Decorate a strip of card and stick it around the rim of the lid to cover the clay seal.

Step 7
Give your snowglobe a shake to see a glittery snowstorm swirling round Jack Frost's Ice Castle!

Magical Friends

The Magical Animal Fairies have some very special animal friends! Read the clues and then draw a line to connect each fairy to her special animal.

Ashley's magical animal can breathe fire.

Lara's animal friend has a happy purr.

Erin's flying friend has colourful feathers.

Rihanna's little creature loves to swim in the sea.

Sophia's animal has soft downy feathers.

Leona's animal likes to carry her on his back.

Caitlin's cuddly creature loves the snow and ice.

A Royal Message

King Oberon and Queen Titania have a special message for you! They've used a magical code to disguise the message so mean Jack Frost can't read it. Are you clever enough to crack the code by writing the human letters underneath the fairy letters?

Human letter		Fairy letter
A	=	X
B	=	Y
C	=	Z
D	=	A
E	=	B
F	=	C
G	=	D
H	=	E
I	=	F
J	=	G
K	=	H
L	=	I
M	=	J
N	=	K
O	=	L
P	=	M
Q	=	N
R	=	O
S	=	P
T	=	Q
U	=	R
V	=	S
W	=	T
X	=	U
Y	=	V
Z	=	W

M I B X P B   Z L J B   Q L
_ _ _ _ _ _   _ _ _ _   _ _

X Y X I I   X Q   Q E B
_ _ _ _ _   _ _   _ _ _

M X I X Z B   T B X O
_ _ _ _ _ _   _ _ _ _

V L R O   C X S L R O F Q B
_ _ _ _   _ _ _ _ _ _ _ _ _

M X O Q V   A O B P P
_ _ _ _ _   _ _ _ _ _

53

Part 3

It was time for the Best of Friends Class to begin! King Oberon explained to Rachel and Kirsty that this class was all about the fairy and her animal working together to demonstrate how strong their friendship is.

As the sky above the castle darkened and shimmered, Kirsty and Rachel saw that a magical pool was forming. The Ocean Fairies fluttered high above them. With a nod from the fairies, ocean animals performed a wonderful synchronised-diving show. Each time water was splashed, the watching fairies were covered in sparkling droplets in every colour of the rainbow!

Next, Lexi the Firefly Fairy's fireflies produced an incredible firework display, forming the shapes of all the animals in Fairyland with their lights.

"What a show!" Rachel whispered to Kirsty. "How do we choose a winner?"

The girls had forgotten that there was one animal partnership yet to perform. The goblin and Sid the Slug! Just then, Sid slid along the ground in front of the palace, heading towards the vegetable gardens at quite a speed. The greedy slug just wanted to eat everything in sight! As his goblin ran after him, trying to persuade him to jump through a hoop made of weeds, Sid's slime formed a very slippery surface, causing the goblin to perform all sorts of slides and dives!

Rachel and Kirsty couldn't help but laugh. It was a very funny sight! Soon all the fairies were laughing and even Jack Frost couldn't help chuckling.

Just as the goblin was getting very slimy and cross, Kirsty's little cat Pearl ran towards the slug, causing him to stop in his tracks so his goblin could catch him.

It was time for the judges to make a decision. Who was the winner of each class? The king, queen and girls eventually agreed: all of the animals were winners! And every one was to be presented with a sparkly star to wear on their coats.

However, the royal couple decided that some animals deserved a special mention.

"Sid the Slug is to be awarded a prize for 'most inventive, comic performance'," said the queen with a smile. Sid looked delighted as an enormous pile of cabbage leaves magically appeared in front of him.

"And Buttons and Pearl did such a good job of helping to keep things under control that they are to be awarded a special 'Friends of Fairyland' prize!" said the king.

Wonderful new collars, glittering with fairy magic, appeared on Buttons and Pearl.

"But," continued the king, "the most important lesson we have learnt is that all animals are special, even if they are different."

The girls smiled at each other. What a magical adventure they'd had at the Fairyland Animal Show! But now it was time for them to go home. Kirsty and Rachel waved to their fairy friends and picked up their clever pets. With a pinch of fairy dust from their treasured lockets, the girls were transported back to Kirsty's bedroom.

"We really are the luckiest girls in the whole world!" Kirsty laughed as she tickled Pearl under her chin.

"We are," agreed Rachel, patting Buttons. "Not only do we have the most magical adventures, but we also have the best animal friends in the world!"

The End

Frost vs the Fashion Fairies!

Ask up to three friends to play with you. Use a counter to move around the board. Follow the instructions on each space. The winner is the one who gets to the fashion show first!

1 START

2

3
Jack Frost throws his huge sunglasses at you! You trip and **MISS A TURN**

17
A goblin throws mud on your favourite outfit. **GO BACK TO START** to change.

15
Queen Titania grants you a wish! **THROW AGAIN**

16

18

19

20
You stop to chat. **MISS A TURN**

21

22
Destiny the Pop Star Fairy distracts the goblins. **MOVE ON 3 PLACES**

23

24
Flora the Fancy Dress Fairy lends you a costume to sneak past Jack Frost! **MOVE TO 28**

Ever since Jack Frost designed his Ice Blue clothing range, he thinks he's the most fashionable creature in the world! So he's determined to stop the Fashion Fairies from hosting an important Fairyland fashion show. Can you help the fairies to reach the show on time?

4

5

6
Phoebe the Fashion Fairy waves her wand and lends a hand!
MOVE ON TO 11

7

8

9

14

13
Jack Frost has been distracted by his own fabulous reflection!
MOVE ON TO 19

12

11

10
A naughty goblin steals your pass for the fashion show. **GO BACK TO 4** to find it.

26

27
Jack Frost throws an ice bolt at you.
GO BACK TO 16

25

28

29

finish
30

Goblins Go Ga-Ga!

In Jennifer the Babysitter Fairy's story, the silly goblins disguised themselves as fairy babies! Can you colour in this picture of the green creatures and the real fairy babies?

Dressed for Dancing!

Vanessa the Dance Steps Fairy is getting ready to teach some dance moves to some of her fairy friends! Can you design the perfect outfit for her to wear?

Hello again, Fairy Friend!

We hope you've enjoyed our annual, we've loved spending time with you! Thank you so much for finding all of our sweet treats, it's lovely to have them back with us. You really are a very special friend and we can't wait to see you again soon.

Lots of love and fluttery fairy hugs,

Esme
x

Clara
x

Coco
x

Madeleine
x

Lottie
x

Nina
x

Layla
x

Where did you find the seven magical charms?

1.
2.
3.
4.
5.
6.
7.

Answers

Page 10
Right Royal Words

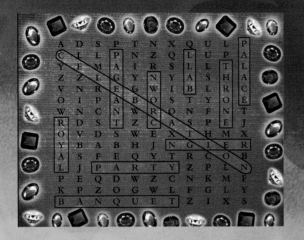

Pages 18 and 19
True or False

1. True
2. False
3. True
4. True
5. False
6. True

Page 31
Green Means Go!

Across

2. Air
5. Garden
6. Coral reef
7. Beach

Down

1. Rainforest
3. Earth
4. River

Page 38
Spot the Difference

Page 52
Magical Friends

Ashley and Sizzle the dragon
Lara and Lucky the black cat
Erin and Giggles the firebird
Rihanna and Bubbles the seahorse
Leona and Twisty the unicorn
Sophia and Belle the snow swan
Caitlin and Crystal the ice bear

Page 53
A Royal Message!

Please come to a ball at the palace!
Wear your favourite party dress.

The Sweet Fairies' magical
charms were on these pages:

10, 18, 29, 35, 38, 46, 57

Have you read them all?

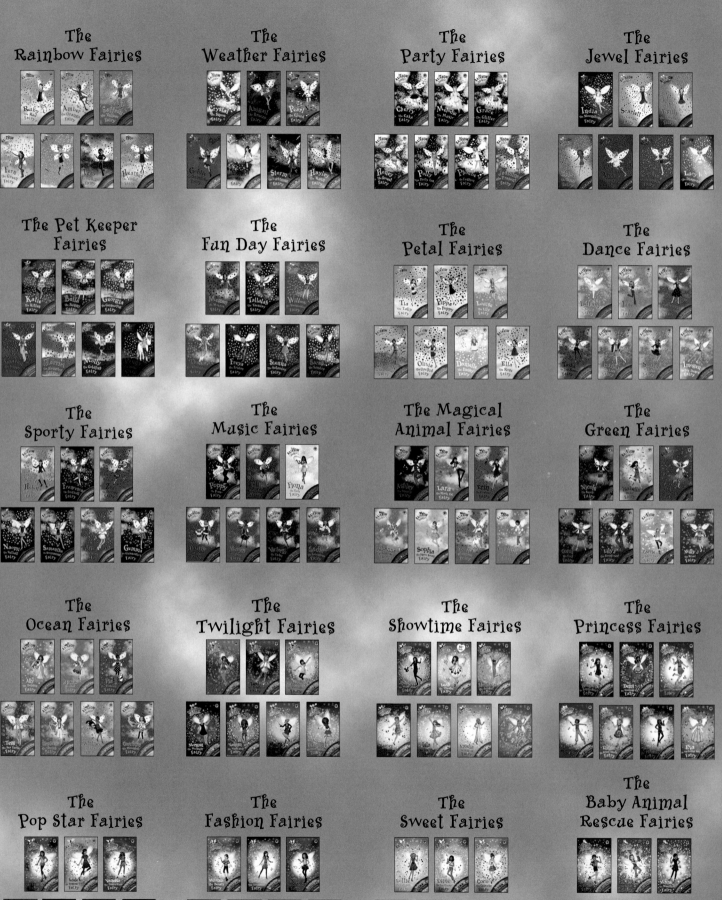

The Rainbow Fairies

The Weather Fairies

The Party Fairies

The Jewel Fairies

The Pet Keeper Fairies

The Fun Day Fairies

The Petal Fairies

The Dance Fairies

The Sporty Fairies

The Music Fairies

The Magical Animal Fairies

The Green Fairies

The Ocean Fairies

The Twilight Fairies

The Showtime Fairies

The Princess Fairies

The Pop Star Fairies

The Fashion Fairies

The Sweet Fairies

The Baby Animal Rescue Fairies